Snowball Moon

For Hannah, the original snow angel
—FCS

For Adelaide and Delia
—TB

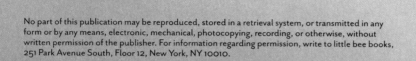

ISBN 978-1-338-26504-0

Text copyright © 2017 by Fran Cannon Slayton. Illustrations copyright © 2017 by Tracy Bishop. All rights reserved. Published by Scholastic Inc., 557 Broadway, New York, NY 10012, by arrangement with little bee books, a division of Bonnier Publishing. SCHOLASTIC and associated logos are trademarks and/or registered trademarks of Scholastic Inc.

The publisher does not have any control over and does not assume any responsibility for author or third-party websites or their content.

12 11 10 9 8 7 6 5 4   19 20 21 22

Printed in the U.S.A.   40

First Scholastic printing, December 2017

Snowball Moon

BY FRAN CANNON SLAYTON

ILLUSTRATED BY TRACY BISHOP

SCHOLASTIC INC.

Snowy night . . .
firelight.

Cozy flames,
friendly games.

Lights go out –
a scream! A shout!

Every eye
on the sky.

Snowball moon,
bright as noon.

Mittens, boots,
warm snowsuits.

Grab the sled
from the shed.

Race outside
for a ride.

Down the hill,
winter thrill.

Frozen lake –
where's the brake?

Slide and slip . . .
double flip!

Upside down,
spinning 'round.

Get up, sport.

Build a fort.

Snowball fight.
What a night!

Frosty fun,
nearly done.

One more ride . . .

warm inside.

Rosy nose,
icy toes.

Goodbye, snow.
Hot cocoa!

Droopy eyes,
snowflake skies.

Counting sheep . . .
fall asleep.

Sleepyheads,
dreams of sleds.

Come back soon,
snowball moon!

Fran Cannon Slayton grew up in Manassas, Virginia, hoping for snow days off from school. After graduating from the University of Virginia (where she once skied on the lawn in front of Thomas Jefferson's famous Rotunda after a huge snowstorm), Fran worked as a prosecutor and legal publisher before becoming a children's book author. Fran lives with her husband, daughter, and a very furry dog in Virginia.

Tracy Bishop grew up on a US Army base just outside of Tokyo, Japan. After working in design at a children's museum, she left to become a full-time illustrator for children's books. Tracy now lives in San Jose, California, where her daily inspirations are her son, husband, and a hairy dog appropriately named Harry. When she's not working, you'll find her reading, collecting picture books, knitting, or tinkering on her computer.